The Electronic Chart

The Electronic Chart

Fundamentals, Functions, Data and other Essentials
A Textbook for ECDIS Use and Training
(3rd, revised and updated edition)

Horst Hecht
Bernhard Berking
Mathias Jonas
Lee Alexander

Horst Hecht / Bernhard Berking / Mathias Jonas / Lee Alexander

The Electronic Chart
Fundamentals, Functions, Data and other Essentials
A Textbook for ECDIS Use and Training
(3rd, revised and updated edition)

Lay-out	:	Ten Brink, Meppel, The Netherlands
Printing company	:	Ten Brink, Meppel, The Netherlands
Publisher	:	Geomares Publishing, Lemmer, The Netherlands

ISBN/EAN: 978-90-806205-8-2

© 2011, Geomares Publishing, Lemmer, The Netherlands

Contents

PART A

Fundamentals
Chapter 1-6

paper nautical chart on the screen. As an interactive navigation information system, it has the potential for displaying all necessary chart and navigation-related information required for the safe and efficient operation of a vessel. A system fulfilling agreed specifications of the International Maritime Organization (IMO) to meet these requirements is termed Electronic Chart Display and Information System (ECDIS).

The following hypothetical voyage of a ship equipped with a modern bridge (Figure 1.1) illustrates the use and value of an electronic chart system.

1.2   Coming a Long Way

M/V 'ECDIS EXPRESS' (length 190 m, draught 8.9 m) – equipped with an **ECDIS** as an embedded component of an **Integrated Navigation System (INS)** – has successfully crossed the ocean and is now navigating the restricted waters of the continental shelf. The passage was speedy – thanks to the automated route planning which considered tides and currents as well as wind and wave forecasts for its calculations. The resulting proposed route taken was safe and efficient. The embedded automatic **Track Control** performed along the route legs connecting the planned **Waypoints** and the vessel was able to travel consistently 1 knot faster then on previous voyages, on the same fuel load. The optimized route itself had been transmitted to the chart service supplier ashore shortly before departure which in turn fed the vessel with the newest digital chart products which might be required along the intended track. All chart oriented and textual nautical information needed for the situation at hand was accessible instantly on request and, if appropriate, transmitted to the front of bridge ECDIS for the execution of the voyage.

1.3   Challenged by Complexity

As the ship approaches the coast, it prepares to enter pilotage waters and later, an unfamiliar port. Not only is this the first time that the ship has ever entered this port, but the fairway is difficult and there is heavy shipping traffic. In addition to being a dark winter afternoon, the weather is poor. There is a strong onshore wind and a heavy sea-state. Visibility is impaired by rain, and the radar display is affected by sea clutter. The time is 14:00 hrs. The ship's arrival into the port is planned for 19:30 hrs. To do this successfully, the ship must pass through a critical shallow water area between 17:30 hrs and 17:50 hrs. The Watch Officer on the bridge gives his full attention to the navigation task, including keeping a sharp lookout for other vessels. At the central 'conning station', alongside the radar console and other navigation and communication devices, is a high-resolution colour monitor serving as an electronic chart display (Figure 1.2). Using the electronic chart as an integrated navigation system, the Watch Officer is able to focus his attention on overall situational awareness without having to spend time running between the chart table, a position-fixing device, the radar and the Automatic Identification System (AIS).

1.4   Record of the Voyage

14:00   The monitor displays a colour **Chart image** of the area showing the **Coastlines, Safe and Shallow Water Areas, Aids-to-navigation (e.g. buoys)** etc. The contour line of 10 m, which is based on the current draught of the vessel, is clearly emphasised as own ship's '**Safety Contour**'. The electronic chart display is free from unnecessary and cluttering information (Figure 1.3). Only the information that the Watch Officer considers important is shown. For clarity, other information that is not necessary for the task-at-hand have been tempo-arily removed by him from the screen. As to the vessel's voyage, the electronic chart system shows the **Way-points** and the **Planned Route** in the run-up to the coast. Own ship is represented by a small symbol. Its position (previously requiring laborious calculations before being plotted on the paper chart) is continually determined by a Global Positioning System (GPS) receiver, and automatically displayed. The ship's symbol 'sails' across the electronic chart display in **Real-time** and in true motion – at it's true-to-scale speed (18 knots). The ship's position on the electronic chart is refreshed every second, and an adjacent

Figure 1.2: Watch Officer navigating with an electronic chart. Source: Sperry Marine.

charted area is displayed. All of this is done automatically. There is no need to change charts!

14:30   The vessel continues its approach the port of destination. The **Radar Image** is overlaid in green colour on the electronic chart display, and the radar image of the coastline closely matches that of the charted shoreline. This additional position confirmation provides increased confidence to the Watch Officer regarding the ship's position and way ahead for a safe transit. Currently, there are five **AIS targets** on the chart display – each with vectors indicating direction and speed. The target on the starboard side is approaching on a collision course (CPA[1] = 0.2 nm, TCPA[2] = 5 min). The values are confirmed by the matching radar echos. The Watch Officer quickly recognises that the vessel will come dangerously close to own ship. As the burdened vessel, the Watch Officer performs the necessary collision avoidance manoeuvre. The electronic chart display clearly shows that the manoeuvre space is sufficient. The ship returns to its previous course.

15:00   As the ship nears the coast, it continues to use the automatic pilot for **Track Control**. The Watch Officer closely monitors the track-keeping – including the planned radius of turn (0.5 nm) – on the electronic chart. With 5-10 m accuracy provided by the Differential GPS (DGPS) positioning system, any deviation from the planned route is quickly shown. Further-

---

1   CPA = closest point of approach
2   TCPA = time to closest point of approach

full sequence of chart visualisations along the settings been used for and as seen by the operator. Systems may also have a colour printer attached that can reproduce – ON DEMAND, the actual screen images. Advanced products used in integrated bridge concepts provide an interface between the electronic chart system and an external voyage date recorder (VDR) as required for the majority of SOLAS vessels.

Different types of installations

Depending on the type of vessel and the preference of the shipowner or operator, electronic chart system installations can vary considerably. Depending on application and implementa- tion, there can be a single system, dual or even multiple installations. Even a single installation can have several monitors connected to the central processing hardware. These can operate either as slave units or master units that take over the operation of the entire system. Another option could involve the installation of several mutually-independent terminals which are all interfaced to a common central processing unit with its assigned data storage and interfaces. Fully-redundant (dual) and multiple installations consist of identical sets of equipment with their own central processing units, data storage and navigational interfaces. These types of sys- tems usually share the same electronic chart data and sensor data over a network (e.g. Ethernet or CAN-Bus).

2.2   Electronic Chart Data

An electronic chart system has an enormous capacity for data storage, retrieval and display. These stored data are the 'knowledge base' of the system. They contain all the geographic, hydrographic and geophysical information for the area, the marine traffic arrangements and the administrative regulations that are also shown on paper charts as well as described and illustrated in relevant printed nautical publications. For this reason, a distinction should be made between paper nautical charts and electronic navigational chart data. Paper nautical charts contain only a selected amount of information, while electronic chart data can contain a far greater amount and content of data.

Additional navigational data

In addition to the types of nautical data traditionally found in nautical publications, electronic chart systems may contain other 'navigational chart' data. However, even the term 'naviga- tional' may not fully indicate the fact that other types of information normally found in numerous sources, can also be contained in the electronic chart dataset. For instance, tidal constituents, explanatory texts and even digital photographs can be stored as part of the electronic chart display system 'knowledge base.' Temporal (i.e. time-varying) data such as ice coverage, current flow, wind direction, or meteorological events can be stored as layers of information that are periodically received and displayed as part of the electronic chart display. Finally, operational data pertaining to the ship such as planned route, waypoints and past-track is another type of navigation-related information. The e-Navigation strategy currently under development under the auspices of IMO particularly addresses the harmonized collection, integration, exchange, presentation and analysis of such maritime information onboard using the electronic chart as the base technology [IMO NAV, 2010]. The impact of this strategy to the future role of ECDIS within the navigation environment is further elaborated in Chapter 24.

operator action. This is especially important when a chart is overloaded with information, or when a 'Display base' has been called up and some important information is missing.

---

1   **Display base** (to be permanently shown on the ECDIS display, consisting of):
.1   coastline (high water);
.2   own ship's safety contour;
.3   isolated underwater dangers of depths less than the safety contour which lie within the safe waters defined by the safety contour;
.4   isolated dangers which lie within the safe water defined by the safety contour, such as fixed structures, overhead wires, etc.;
.5   scale, range and north arrow;
.6   units of depth and height; and
.7   display mode.

---

2   **Standard display** (consisting of):
.1   display base
.2   drying line
.3   buoys, beacons, other aids to navigation and fixed structures
.4   boundaries of fairways, channels, etc.
.5   visual and radar conspicuous features
.6   prohibited and restricted areas
.7   chart scale boundaries
.8   indication of cautionary notes
.9   ships' routing systems and ferry routes
.10   archipelagic sea lanes

---

3   **All other information** (to be displayed individually on demand, for example):
.1   spot soundings
.2   submarine cables and pipelines
.3   details of all isolated dangers
.4   details of aids to navigation
.5   contents of cautionary notes
.6   ENC edition date
.7   most recent chart update number
.8   magnetic variation
.9   graticule
.10   place names

Table 9.2 (a-c): *Categories of SENC information available for display during route planning and route monitoring. a) '1 Display base', b) '2 Standard display'; c) '3 All other Information'. Source: IMO ECDIS Performance Standards [IMO ECDIS PS – App. 2, 2006].*

9.4   Scale, Range and Usage

The navigator can change the display scale by appropriate steps, e.g. by means of either chart scale values or ranges in nautical miles. By selecting a certain range at a certain state of the voyage, he decides whether the chart display is more appropriate for giving a better overview or by providing more details. He is not bothered with loading new and better-scaled charts from the SENC because the ECDIS makes use of the advantage of a seamless database and provides automatically the proper chart data for a certain range. Some ECDIS even provide the automatic (programmed) selection of an ENC of the most appropriate scale – based on the ship's position and motion.

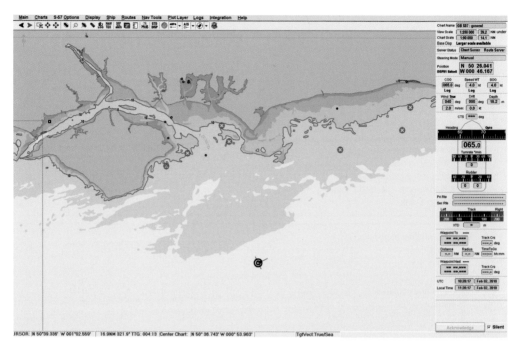

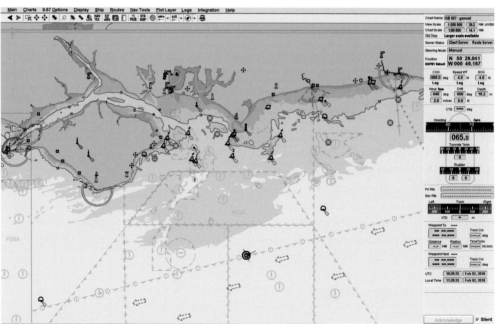

Figure 9.4.a and b: Display categories. a) Top: 'Display base'. b) Centre: 'Standard display'.
Source: Raytheon Anschütz and UKHO (data).

(1) Overview – 'range' instead 'scale'
The scale of an electronic chart being displayed (both the compilation scale of the chart and the current screen-related scale) is up to the user to decide. It could be from a general track overview chart (small scale) to a highly detailed harbour plan (large scale). It is possible to

– his own position,
– all charted objects and obstacles,
– all other vessels in the area.

Figures 12.4, 12.5 and 12.6 show typical radar 'overlays' with coastlines, own ship and several radar targets shown during day and night time situations.

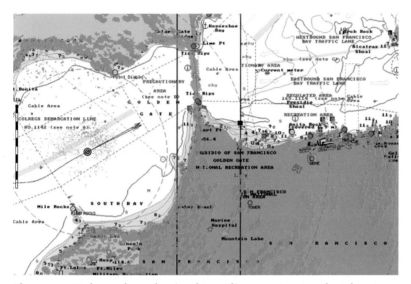

Figure 12.4: *Radar overlay – showing the coastline, some targets, other relevant objects (Golden Gate Bridge) and, unfortunately, a certain amount of clutter. Range 6 nm (scale 1:30,000). Sea area: San Francisco. Source: TRANSAS and NOAA (data).*

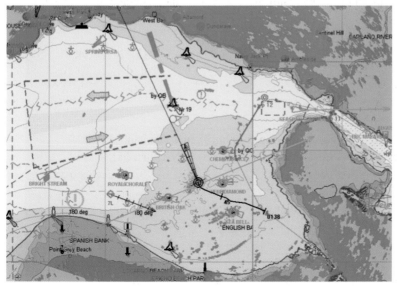

Figure 12.5: *Radar overlay – showing the coastline, some targets, a racon and, unfortunately, a certain amount of clutter. Sea area: Vancouver. Source: OSL.*

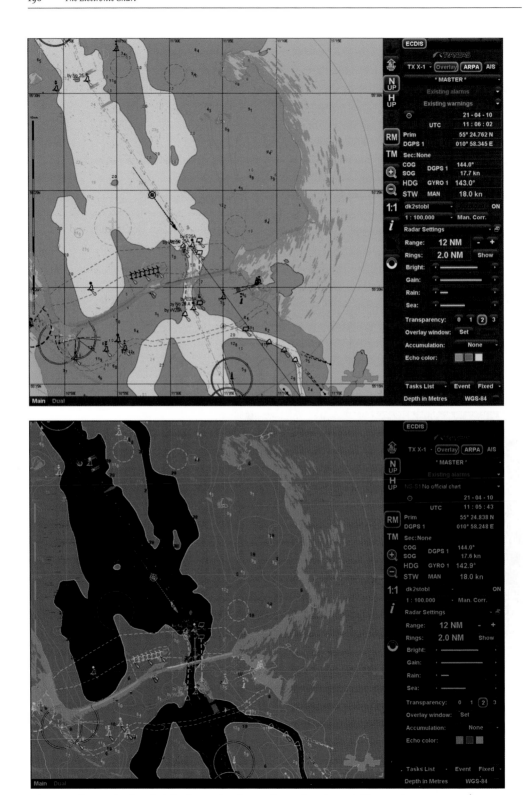

Figure 12.6: Day (top) and night (bottom) radar overlay – showing coastlines and targets.
Sea area: Denmark/Sweden. Source: TRANSAS and DK/S HOs (data).

12.1.4 POSITION MONITORING

The most important navigational use of the ECDIS radar overlay is that it allows a quick cross-check of the ship's position. If ground-fixed objects such as (suitable) coast lines or other reference targets of the radar picture and of the electronic chart do not match (i.e. the whole radar picture is shifted) as shown in Figure 12.7, this is a clear indication that the ship's position (e.g. by GPS; potentially the horizontal datum) is incorrect. In practice, the ECDIS radar overlay provides a continuous and easy-to-use radar fix in which radar takes the role of a second independent position fixing system. If the two pictures were rotated against each other, e.g. for 3°, a course error would become apparent. Generally, differences between chart and radar image provide a chance to detect errors which otherwise might not have been detected at all – although, needless to say, these differences exist also in the separated displays, but they are not so easy to notice. Care has to be taken when using buoys (not ground-fixed) and flat coastlines (no realistic radar image) for the position cross check.

> The navigator should – at least from time to time – overlay the radar on the ECDIS display to check his navigation: If there is
> – a translational offset, there is a position error;
> – a rotational offset, there is a course error.

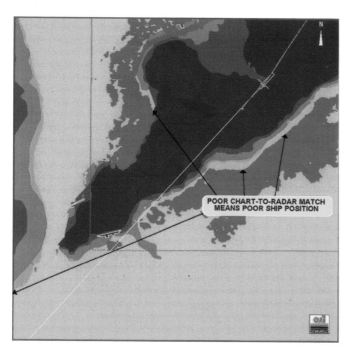

POOR CHART-TO-RADAR MATCH
MEANS POOR SHIP POSITION

Figure 12.7: *Bad match of electronic chart (here: ECS with vector data) and radar overlay: Coastlines are 'out-of-place'. Clear indication that own ship's position (GPS) is incorrect or chart information is poorly positioned. Sea area: Great Lakes. Source: OSL.*

12.1.5 FURTHER BENEFITS OF THE RADAR OVERLAY

Besides the integration of grounding avoidance and collision avoidance and effective position monitoring, the integration of ECDIS and radar offers a number of significant advantages which are listed in Table 12.1.

	Benefits of ECDIS / Radar Overlay
Collision avoidance	Targets and the area of safe water available for a collision avoidance manoeuvre are readily apparent in one display.
Position monitoring	The radar image in the ECDIS display serves as a continuously independent position fix. It monitors continuously the primary position fixing system (GPS/DGPS).
Target identification	Radar targets can be more easily identified when viewed together with charted information. In particular the identification of objects such as ships in the channel, buoys adjacent to the channel, and vessels lying at anchor is much easier.
Radar performance	The radar-specific limitations (poor resolution, shading) are minimised. Radar targets lying close together, in narrow waterways, or under bridges can be more recognised.
Shifted objects	The set of navigation buoys (the direction of the current flow or the off-place of a buoy) can be determined by comparing their actual (radar) and charted (ECDIS) position.
False fairway detection	Ships travelling on the wrong side of a traffic separation zone (TSZ) can be recognised as such.
Error detection	Errors caused by different reference systems and sensor data (e.g. north orientation of both 'images', course differences, speed through water or over ground) can be more easily recognised on an integrated display.
Mutual check	The overlaid ECDIS and radar images serve to verify one another. As long as the relevant symbols correlate with each other, the functional efficiency of ECDIS and radar is achieved.
Reduced errors	Human errors (e.g. when transferring information from one system to another) are reduced.
Reduced workload	Radar bearings and distances need not be manually entered on a chart. The Watch Officer is relieved of this and other routine work.
System redundancy	Flexibility and redundancy of the two systems (i.e. ECDIS and radar) are enhanced.

Table 12.1: *Some essential benefits of integrating ECDIS and radar information.*

Identification of objects
Because relevant objects appear both on the electronic chart and on the radar overlay, they can be compared directly with each other. Example: If a dark green radar paint does not correspond with any object on the electronic chart, it is immediately interpreted as a ship or another object which means a potential danger to the own ship and requires special attention.

Detection of irregularities
Figure 12.8 shows a radar overlay in which one buoy (top; starboard side) is 'out-of-place' whereas all others buoys and the fixed coast-lines are 'in place'. Obviously, it may be concluded that this buoy has moved or that its coordinates in the data base are incorrect. If all (!) the buoys were 'out-of-place', this could most easily be explained by current.

12.2.2   AIS SYMBOLOGY AND USE OF AIS

Practical experiences gained with AIS operation in the introductory phase have evidently shown the inevitable need for a harmonised presentation of all navigation related information provided from various sources such as Radar, ARPA, ECDIS and AIS, and processed together on the various navigational displays on the ships bridge.

Device independent symbols

As a result, a consistent solution was determined by IMO [IMO NavDis P., 2004] for the device independent presentation of the own ship symbol, radar symbols and AIS symbols. These three classes of symbols are discriminated by shape, e.g., radar symbols based on a circle, and AIS symbols based on an oriented triangle. For radar and AIS targets the functional state, e.g., danger state, is coded consistently by applying additional attributes to the base symbol. The resulting definition of AIS-symbology for the visualisation of AIS equipped vessels] and the operational conditions connected with it are shown in Tables 12.4. Figure 12.10 gives an impression how AIS target symbols look like on a chart display.

Static	Dynamic	Voyage related
MMSI – Maritime Mobile Service Identity	Ship's position with accuracy indication and integrity status	Ship's draught
Call sign & name	Time in UTC	Hazardous cargo
IMO number	Course over ground	Destination and estimated time of arrival
Length and beam	Speed over ground	Route plan
Type of ship	Heading	
Location of position-fixing antenna on the ship and ships dimensions	Navigational status (e.g. underway by engines, not under command, at anchor, moored, etc)	
	Rate of turn	

Table 12.2: *Various types of information transmitted by each shipborne AIS radio transponder.*

Update rate of AIS	
Static information:	every 6 min. and on request
Dynamic Information:	dependent on speed and course alteration (see table 12.2)
Voyage related information	every 6min, when data has been amended, and on request
Safety-related message:	As required

Table 12.3: *Update rates of AIS dependent from the type of information transferred.*

Topic	Symbol	Description
AIS Target (sleeping)		– Isosceles, acute-angled triangle. – Triangle oriented by heading, or COG if heading missing. – Reported position to be located at centre and half the height of the triangle. – Symbol of the sleeping target to be smaller than that of the activated target.
Activated AIS Target Including Dangerous Target		– Isosceles, acute-angled triangle. – Triangle oriented by heading, or COG if heading missing. – Reported position should be located at centre and half the height of the triangle. – COG/SOG vector to be displayed as dashed line with short dashes with spaces approximately twice the line width. Optionally, time increments may be marked along the vector. – Heading to be displayed as solid line thinner than speed vector line style, length twice of the length of the triangle symbol. Origin of the heading line is the apex of the triangle. – The turn to be indicated by a flag of fixed length added to heading line. – A path predictor may be provided as curved vector. – For a "Dangerous AIS Target", bold, red solid triangle with course and speed vector, flashing until acknowledged.
AIS Target – True Scale Outline		– A true scale outline may be added to the triangle symbol. – Located relative to reported position and according to reported position offsets, beam and length. Oriented along own ship's heading. – Used on small ranges/large scales.
Selected target		– A square indicated by its corners to be drawn around the target symbol.
Lost target		– Triangle with bold solid cross. – Triangle to be oriented per last known value. – Cross has fixed orientation. – Symbol flashes until acknowledged. – Target to be displayed without vector, heading and rate of turn indication.
Target Past Positions		– Dots, equally spaced by time.

Table 12.4: *Mandated AIS target symbolisation [IMO NavSym., 2004].*

TASK: ROUTE PLANNING
- ECDIS planning functions
- IMO passage planning procedures
- Route administration
- Route check against
  - under keel-clearance hazards
  - manoeuvring limits
  - meteorological information

TASK: ROUTE MONITORING
- ECDIS monitoring functions
- ECDIS-radar overlay
- Under-keel clearance alarm
- AIS reports of AtoNs
- Planned track and related data

Optional
- *Tracked radar and AIS targets*
- *SAR and MOB manoeuvres*
- *Tidal, current, weather, ice data*

TASK: COLLISION AVOIDANCE
- Radar functions and data
- ENC database objects
- Target data association
- Target identifier
- Multiple radar signals
  Optional:
  - *True scale ship symbols*
  - *CPA related to real dimensions*
  - *Traffic related object layers*

TASK: NAVIGATION CONTROL DATA
- Data for manual / automatic control:
  - Position, SOG/COG, Heading, ROT
  - Rudder angle, propulsion
  - Set and drift, wind
  - Radius and rate of turn
  - Set and actual values
  - Trend of parameters (if applicable)
  - Mode of control
- External safety-related messages

TASK: STATUS AND DATA
- Mode and status information
- Own ship's motion data
- Editing AIS data to be transmitted
- Received AIS messages
- INS configuration
- Sensor and source information
- NAVTEX

Optional:
- *Tidal, current, weather, ice data*

TASK: ALERT MANAGEMENT
- Alarms, Warnings, Cautions
- Audial and visual mode
- Centralised alarm handling
- Acknowledgement
- Alert escalation

Figure 12.19: Essential INS tasks and their respective functions [IMO INS PS, 2007]: ECDIS-related tasks in blue colour.

– procedures for voyage planning, if applicable adopted by IMO, and
– means for
  - administering the route plan (store and load, export, documentation, protection)
  - checking the route against hazards based on the planned under keel clearance
  - drafting, refining and checking the route plan against manoeuvring limitation, if available in the INS, based on turning radius, rate of turn, wheel-over and course changing points, speed, time, ETAs,
  - drafting and refining the route plan against meteorological information if available in the INS.

Task "Route monitoring"

a) Minimum set of functions

For the task "Route monitoring" (Figure 12.19; top right), an INS provides as a minimum the route monitoring functions and data as specified in Module A and B in the ECDIS performance standards and means for

- taking-over the route plan from the route planning task station, if applicable, and alterations of the route,
- continuous real-time display of own ship's position and motion on the navigational chart,
- optionally overlaying radar video data on the chart to allow position evaluation and object identification,
- determination of deviations between set values and actual values for under keel clearance and initiating an under-keel clearance alarm,
- the display of LAT, LON, heading, COG, SOG, STW, under-keel clearance, ROT (measured or derived from change of heading) and
- if "Track control" is integrated into the INS, the inclusion of the planned track and track related and manoeuvring data.

b) Optional Functions

For navigational purposes, other route-related information on the chart display may be displayed, e.g.

- tracked radar targets and AIS targets,
- AIS binary and safety-related messages, AIS reports of AtoNs,
- weather data and ice data, tidal and current data,
- initiation and monitoring of person-over-board manoeuvres (see below),
- initiation and monitoring of SAR manoeuvres (see below),
- NAVTEX data.

More over, a pre-defined display mode
- for a "search and rescue" situation and
- for a "person-over-board" (POB) situation
may be selected on the route monitoring display.

INS Alert management instead of ECDIS alarms and indications

INS provides a central alert management system which harmonizes the priority (alarms, warnings and cautions) and classification of alerts. The number of alerts is minimized in order to enable the bridge team to devote full attention to the safe navigation of the ship and to immediately identify any abnormal situation.

As a consequence for ECDIS, all "alarms" and "indications" (Chapter 9.13) are taken over by the INS alert management system. This relates
- to all alarms and indications generated by ECDIS itself and
- to all alarms generated by input sensor to ECDIS (e.g. of GPS receiver).

Therefore, neither ECDIS nor the sensors will provide an alert themselves. They are intentionnaly muted. This is achieved by bi-directional communication between the different components of the INS.

RCDS Mode of Operation

As described in Chapter 3, ECDIS is capable of operating in two modes:
1) ECDIS mode when ENCs are used.
2) Raster Chart Display Systems (RCDS) mode where ENCs do not exist and Raster Navigational Chart (RNCs) are used instead.

This Chapter explains the capabilities and limitations of the RCDS mode-of-operation in terms of display-related considerations, route planning, route monitoring, and when integrated with other types of navigational systems. The principal differences between raster and vector data are described in Chapter 4.1.

13.1 RNC: Capabilities and Limitations

The primary advantage of using an RNC instead of relying on a paper nautical chart is that when used with a GPS positioning, ownship's position can be displayed on the RNC in real-time. Also, the official RNC is an exact digital copy (i.e., a raster facsimile) of the paper nautical chart. When automatic RNC updating services are provided, they are analogous to the paper Notice-to-Mariners that are periodically issued to update paper nautical charts.

However, RNCs also have some limitations. When using vector data, it is possible to simplify or reduce the amount of information shown on the display. However, with RNCs all information that is contained in a paper nautical chart is also shown on a RNC. This can result in a rather cluttered display when other types of operational information are also shown (e.g., radar/ARPA, AIS targets, MIOs, AMLs, etc.)

Because of the limitations of the RCDS mode, the use of RNCs for navigation is permitted only under considerable restrictions, see chapter 14.4 for details.

In October 2007, IMO issued revised guidance regarding the differences between RCDS and ECDIS [IMO, RCDS, (1999) 2007]. This guidance falls into four general categories: display-related, route planning, route monitoring, and integration with other navigational systems.

13.1.1 DISPLAY RELATED
- Unlike ENCs that have no displayed boundaries, RNCs are based on paper nautical charts and have boundaries which are evident on the ECDIS display.

- Horizontal and vertical datums and chart projections may differ between RNCs. As such, it is important to understand how the horizontal datum relates to the datum of the position fixing system currently in use (see Chapter 5.1.1). In some instances, this can appear as a shift in position. This difference is most noticeable at grid intersections.
- The orientation of the RCDS display to other than 'chart-up', may affect the readability of chart text and symbols (e.g., course-up, route-up).
- Depending on the producer or source of the RNC, different colours may be used to show similar chart information. There may also be differences in colours used between day and night time.
- An RNC is intended to be used at the scale of the equivalent paper chart. Excessive scale change (e.g., zooming-in or zooming-out) can seriously degrade the displayed image. However, when the RNC is displayed at a larger scale than the equivalent paper nautical chart, the ECDIS display should provide an indication.
- ECDIS provides an indication in the ENC which allows a determination of the quality of hydrographic the data. When using RNCs, the source diagram or the zone of confidence diagram must be consulted.

13.1.2   ROUTE PLANNING

- RNCs do not trigger automatic alarms (e.g., anti-grounding). However, during passage planning, some alarms and indications can be manually generated during route planning. These can include clearing lines, ship safety contour lines, isolated danger markers, and danger areas.
- In some cases, an RNC is not referenced to either WGS-84 or PE 90 geodetic datums. Where this occurs, ECDIS should provide a continuous indication.
- It is not possible to interrogate RNC features in order to gain additional information about charted objects. As such, during route planning, it is necessary to consult all relevant publications (e.g., sailing directions, Coast Pilot, etc.).
- Unless manually-entered during route planning, it is not possible to display ownship's safety contour or safety depth, and then highlight it on the display.

13.1.3   ROUTE MONITORING

- Without selecting different scale charts the look-ahead capability may be limited.
This may lead to inconvenience when determining range and bearing or the identity of distant objects.

13.1.4   INTEGRATION WITH OTHER NAVIGATIONAL SYSTEMS

- The display of RNCs features cannot be simplified by the removal of features to suit a particular navigational circumstance or task-at-hand. In particular, this effects the superimposition of radar/ARPA or display of AIS target information.

13.2   Operational Procedures

While the Performance Standards for RCDS were patterned after those for ECDIS, there are some notable similarities and differences in the operational capability of RCDS in comparison to ECDIS. As specified in Appendix 7 of the IMO Performance Standards for ECDIS, the primary differences for RCDS include:

— When operating in the RCDS mode, an appropriate portfolio of up-to-date paper charts must be carried onboard and be readily available to the mariner (Sec 1.2).
— The contents of the system RNC should be adequate and up-to-date for that part of the voyage not covered by ENC (Sec. 4.2).
— There should always be an indication if the ECDIS equipment is operating in the RCDS mode (Sec. 5.13).
[IMO ECDIS PS (1995) 2006]

The key operational procedures that should be kept in mind when operating in the RCDS mode of operation are listed in Table 13.1. For convenience, this overview is based on what was previously described for ENCs in ECDIS in Chapters 8 – 12.

Chapter/ Section	ECDIS Topic	RCDS mode	Comments (including similarities and differencescompared to ENCs)
8	Chart handling functions	same	— RNCs must be the latest edition, issued by or under the authority of a government-authorized HO. — The contents of the System RNC (SRNC) must be up-to-date for the intended voyage. While this is usually performed via automated RNC updating service, this can also be performed manually by using paper Notice-to-Mariners.
8.1	Chart data: base cells and updates		
1)	Structure	different	Unlike the naming convention for ENCs, the name and number of an RNC corresponds to the paper nautical chart.
2)	Provision of charts and updates	same	—
3)	ENC to SENC	basically similar	An RNC is transformed into a System RNC (SRNC) in the ECDIS equipment, and includes updates to the RNC.
8.2	Charts and permits	basically similar	— Depending on the type and source of the RNCs, a valid permit may be required to access and use the RNC data in the ECDIS equipment. Similar to ENC data, permits can be provided via e-mail, CD, diskette, USB stick, manual keyboard input, or network-based procedures. — It is a prudent practice to check the status or expiration date of the RNC license permits that are required for the intended voyage, prior to getting underway.
8.3	Availability of charts		
1)	Overview	same	Typically, the coverage or availability of RNCs can be viewed on a geographic display.
2)	Selection for display	same	—
8.4	Importing and uploading	similar	— Once it has been determined what portions of the intended route where ENC data is not available, import and upload the necessary RNC data. — If there is a circumstance where neither ENC nor RNC data is available, then a necessary portfolio of paper nautical charts must be used. — Verify that ECDIS has uploaded sufficient chart data for the entire voyage (e.g., ENC and RNCs).

Chapter/ Section	ECDIS Topic	RCDS mode	Comments (including similarities and differencescompared to ENCs)
8.5	Viewing status of updates	similar	In conjunction with viewing the status of ENC updates, verify that all RNC updates have been applied (e.g., either automated or manual). This is usually performed by viewing updates that are "highlighted" on the ECDIS display.
8.6	Manual updating	same	—
9	**Chart display-related functions and tools**	same	There should always be an indication on the ECDIS display that the system is operating in the RCDS mode.
9.1	Selection of the sea area		
1)	Chart around own ship	similar	For most RCDS equipment, individual charts usually have to be called up. For convenience, several charts can be loaded in advance.
2)	Selecting charts of other sea areas	same	—
9.2	Chart status and quality		
1)	Indication of chart data status	similar	It should always be possible to distinguish between those areas that are covered by ENCs and those by RNCs.
2)	Quality of chart data	different	The source diagram or zone of confidence diagram (if provided) must be used.
3)	Inappropriate range/scale	similar	When the RNC is displayed at a larger scale that the equivalent paper chart, ECDIS should provide an indication.
9.3	Display of data	different	There is no way chose the amount of chart data to be displayed (e.g., base, standard, and 'all other information').
9.4	Scale, range and usage	similar	While it is possible to change the display scale of the RNC, it may be necessary to re-adjust the scale of the display when crossing an adjacent chart boundary.
1)	Overview – 'range' instead 'scale'	same	—
2)	'Range' decides whether a buoy is displayed	different	Unlike ENC data that has the attribute 'SCAMIN', with an RNC there is no automatic 'generalization' that occurs when range (or scale) is changed.
3)	'Overscale' and 'underscale'	different	Unlike ENC display, no under/overscale indication is provided. However, at underscale the raster data appears very cluttered while at overscale, the raster display may begin show individual pixels.
9.5	Areas for which special conditions exist	different	Function not available.
9.6	'Pick' report: detailed background information		Function not available.

Chapter/ Section	ECDIS Topic	RCDS mode	Comments (including similarities and differencescompared to ENCs)
9.7	Depth information and safety contour	different	Function not available.
9.8	ECDIS symbols: Mariner's selection and identification		
1)	Chart symbols	different	The RNC chart symbols are the same as those on the paper nautical chart.
2)	Scaleable ship symbol	same	—
3)	Catalogue of symbols (Chart 1)	same	—
9.9	Mariner's notes and danger highlights	same	—
9.10	Day and night display	similar	There are two basic displays of RNCs: day and night. The daytime colours are similar in appearance to those on a paper chart. Night-time colours are similar but convert the white back ground colours to a darker shade (e.g., grey).
9.11	Mode of presentation		
1)	True and relative motion	same	—
2)	North-up and course-up/ head-up presentation	similar	North-up mode is generally used in order to read any text information.
9.12	Navigational tools	same	—
9.13	Alarms and status indications	similar	Some of the Alarms and Indication for ECDIS are not available in the RCDS Mode. See Table 13.2 for the specific list of "Alarms and Indicators in the RCDS Mode of Operation"

Chapter/ Section	ECDIS Topic	RCDS mode	Comments (including similarities and differences compared to ENCs)
10	**Route planning functions**		
10.1	Bridge procedures for route planning	similar	With some exceptions (e.g., use of 'pick reports' or highlight caution areas), the route planning functions are similar to that of ECDIS.
10.2	Constructing the draft route by graphic editor	same	—
10.3	Refining the route		
1)	Increasing scale	same	—
2)	Waypoint and leg data	same	—
3)	Insertion of information	same	—
4)	Editing	same	—
10.4	Automatic 'route check'		
.1	Parameter setting for automatic 'route check'	similar	With some exceptions (e.g., across ownship safety contour, spot sounding, vertical draft, etc.), most settings are similar to that of ECDIS.
.2	Route check and route correction	similar	With some exceptions (e.g., across ownship safety contour, spot sounding, vertical draft, etc.), the automatic checks are similar to that of ECDIS.
10.5	Final route and waypoint list		
1)	Accepting the route	same	—
2)	Waypoint list	same	—
10.6	Route management		
1)	Storing and administering routes	same	—
2)	Re-use of existing route from library	same	—

Chapter/ Section	ECDIS Topic	RCDS mode	Comments (including similarities and differencescompared to ENCs)
11	**Route monitoring functions**		
11.1	Bridge procedures for route monitoring	similar	With some exceptions (e.g., display of safety-related objects, ships safety contour, or caution areas), the route monitoring functions are similar to that of ECDIS.
11.2	Modes and settings for route monitoring	similar	With some exceptions (e.g., look ahead for ENC objects, ships safety contour, or caution areas), the modes and setting functions are similar to that of ECDIS.
11.3	Automatic position display and limits (for ownship)	same	—
.1	Automatic real-time display	same	—
.2	Quality require-ments of position-fixing within ECDIS	same	—
.3	Accuracy: Systematic and statistical errors	same	—
.4	Available position-fixing systems	same	—
.5	Risks and effects of inaccurate posi-tion determination	same	—
11.4	Position monitoring by the OOW	same	—
.1	Visual position monitoring in the ECDIS display	same	—
.2	Automatic alarms and indications	same	—
.3	Active position monitoring by the OOW	same	—
11.5	Display of own-ship's motion	same	—
.1	Course and speed sensors	same	—
.2	Vectors	same	—
11.6	Ship and environ-mental data	same	—

Chapter/ Section	ECDIS Topic	RCDS mode	Comments (including similarities and differencescompared to ENCs)
11.7	'Look ahead' function and alarms		
.1	ENC-related alarms	different	Not available.
.2	'Anti-grounding' alarms and parameter setting	different	Not available.
.3	'Anti-grounding' alarm messages	different	Not available.
.4	'Unjustified' ECDIS alarm	different	Not available.
11.8	Sensor and track control and other alarms and indications	similar	See Table 13.2 for "Alarms and Indicators in the RCDS Mode of Operation"
11.9	Predicting own ship's movement	same	—
11.10	ECDIS voyage recording	similar	The ECDIS must keep a log of the ENC and RNC data that was used during the voyage.
11.11	Additional functions for route monitoring	similar	Most additional ECDIS functions are also available in the RCDS mode.

PART E

Other Essential ECDIS Aspects
Chapter 19-24

21.3.1   ECDIS TEST STANDARDS BY IEC

At the request of IMO, the International Electrotechnical Commission (IEC) established the operational methods of testing for an IMO-compliant ECDIS. For each of the sections contained in the IMO Performance Standards for ECDIS, IEC developed appropriate test requirements, procedures and required test results. This also applies to each of the various ECDIS-related specifications provided in the current versions of IHO S-52 and IHO S-57, and associated appendices. The IEC ECDIS Test Standard (*Operational and Performance Requirements: Methods of Testing and Required Test Results*) are contained in IEC Publication 61174 [IEC 61174, (1998) 2008].

21.3.2   ECS TESTING

For most maritime nations, electronic chart systems (ECS) can be used for navigation purposes on non-SOLAS vessels without special tests or approval. However, some maritime nations require that any vessel operating under its flag use equipment that has been type-approved. For instance, German national laws require testing and approval of any type of electronic chart system (whether ECDIS or ECS) when it is to be installed on a ship under the German flag. The tests performed by BSH (Bundesamt für Seeschifffahrt und Hydrographie), the Federal Maritime and Hydrographic Agency of Germany are aligned to those of ECDIS testing but do not ask for operation of official S-57 data and presentation according to S-52 standard of IHO. The test compliance document that is issued explicitly states:
– the approval does not cover the completeness, correctness and validity of the data base in use,
– the system may be used for navigation only in connection with, and in addition to, the paper charts which are required to be carried onboard.

21.4   Legal Liability

There is a significant difference between what ships are required to carry under national regulations (e.g., based on national laws or International Conventions), and a shipping company's responsibility or legal liability in the event of a 'preventable' shipping casualty. Conformance to regulations does not necessarily preclude a court of law finding of negligence, fault, or legal liability. Based on the concept of 'seaworthiness' and 'due diligence', the findings of a court can supersede regulatory requirements. There have been some recent shipping incidents when ECDIS was a factor:
– august 2004 – A cross-channed ferry grounded while approaching the port entrance. ECDIS safety features had not been correctly enabled,
– january 2008 – A container vessel grounded on Varne Bank. Although a type-approved ECDIS was installed, depth contours were not properly set and safety features (e.g., alarms and indicators) were not enabled,
– may 2008 – A cargo vessel grounded of the east coast of England. Although a type-approved ECDIS was installed, track monitoring was not conducted, safety features were not enabled, and there was an inadequately trained crew.

A recent incident that occured in the English Channel provides an example of what can go wrong when an ECDIS is not properly used. On 31 January 2008, the ro-ro passenger ferry, *Pride of Canterbury* grounded on a charted wreck in an area known as 'The Downs' off Deal,

Kent. As described in the UK Marine Accident Investigation Branch Report [PoC InvRep, 2009], the vessel had been in the area for over four hours when the bridge team became distracted by a fire alarm and numerous telephone calls. The vessel overshot the northern limit of the safe area before the turn was started. The officer-of-the-watch (OOW) became aware that the vessel was passing close to a charted shoal, but he was unaware that there was a charted wreck on the shoal. The officer was navigating by eye and referring to the ECDIS display which was situated at the front of the bridge. However, he was untrained in the use and limitations of the system. The wreck would not have been displayed on the ECDIS due to the user settings in use at the time. A paper chart was available, but positions had only been plotted on it sporadically, and it was not referred to at the crucial time.

The over-riding legal consideration affecting any type of maritime shipping activity involves such fundamental matters as the duty to exercise 'due diligence', 'seaworthiness', and 'prudent seamanship.' Beyond regulatory compliance, the most relevant issue is the fulfilment of a legal duty 'to take care'. As it relates to the installation and use of any type of shipboard navigation system, if a maritime incident resulting in environmental pollution were to occur, a shipowner may be deemed responsible for damage or clean-up costs if the court determined that the accident was 'preventable'(e.g., by the use of ECDIS or ECS).

The advent of ECDIS in an already complex legal world has introduced uncertainties revolving around new technology, numerous players, re-defined roles and legal responsibilities. In some respects, the functional capability of ECDIS will govern its legal impact. However, there is no definitive legal answer to the fundamental question: *Is ECDIS really just an electronic sea chart, or is it an entirely new navigational tool?* This distinction may determine whether there exists a duty to take care, and if so, what is the standard of care to which various entities will be held. Clearly, there are differences in perceptions, roles, and responsibilities between the Hydrographic Office, an electronic chart manufacturer, a maritime safety administration, and the shipowner/mariner.

21.4.1 HYDROGRAPHIC OFFICES

In a majority of the world's major waterways, a ship is not considered seaworthy unless it carries an adequate portfolio of charts. In the past, 'adequate charts' were paper nautical charts issued or approved by national Hydrographic Office. In general, it is the responsibility of a Hydrographic Office to ensure that information shown on a chart is an accurate and adequate depiction of the facts. The date of the survey, the scale and accuracy of the data, the date the last edition was published, and the frequency of the updating service are all a responsibility of the government. If producing a nautical chart to ensure safety-of-navigation, the Hydrographic Office must clearly describe any specific dangers that arise from the use of the product and warn of the inherent limitations. The standard of care necessary to produce charts is influenced by the degree of reliance by the mariner and the extent of potential damages if an incident occurs. While this may be fairly straightforward for a paper nautical chart, it is less clear how this should be accomplished in terms of an electronic chart database issued for use with ECDIS or ECS.

Electronic Charting has created a new dilemma for the Hydrographic Office and the user. The amount of time and effort required to produce ENCs has proven to be more difficult than many

Depending on complexity (e.g., stand-lone-system vs. integrated navigation system), the approximate cost of a type-approved ECDIS equipment is:

hardware and software $ 20,000 to $ 100,000
ENC data/services $ 500 to $ 15,000

Depending on whether a new build or retrofit, there is usually an additional cost for installation. There can also be a significant, ongoing maintenance costs (hardware, software and data) that are difficult to quantify.

Other costs associated with purchasing and installing an ECDIS include:
– whether as a stand-alone console or a component of an integrated navigation system
   (e.g., an ECDIS as a multi-functional display component of an integrated bridge),
– installation and integration with other systems and sensors,
– equipment training/bridge simulator.

22.2   Operational Costs

In contrast to the one-time purchase/installation cost, there are on-going operational costs associated with the use of ECDIS. Similar to initial purchase costs, it is useful to first look at the costs associated with the use of paper charts and other nautical publications.

22.2.1   PAPER NAUTICAL CHARTS
According to reports of shipowners and chart agents, the annual cost of supplying current editions of paper charts, Notice to Mariners (NtM), and other nautical chart publications can range from $ 3,000 - $ 6,000 per year per vessel.

Updating paper charts through the use of printed NtMs is a time-consuming process. Based on the experience of mariners who actually perform this task, manual updating of paper charts takes 4-8 hours per week for a coastal vessel, 8-21 hours per week for regular line sailing, and 8-20 hours per week for a tramp steamer. Based on a rate of $25 per hour, the annual man-power cost of performing manual updating of paper charts would be:

Coastal vessel $ 5,000 to $ 10,000
Ocean-going vessel $ 10,000 to $ 16,000
Tramp steamer $ 10,000 to $ 26,000

One chart agent (Marine Press of Canada) provides a digital NtM updating service that enables ships to receive nautical chart update service both in port and at-sea. Called Digitrace®, the production and provision of chart correction traces in digital format significantly reduces the time required for manual updating of paper charts. Another chart agent (ChartCo) provides digital NtM and paper chart corrections delivery directly to ships at sea by means of a satellite communication broadcast (Inmarsat A, B or Fleet77). If a vessel already has a satellite communications installed for other purposes, then this could be an option. However, most satellite communications are relatively narrow band, and the cost of receiving ENC updates can be expensive.

22.2.2   ELECTRONIC CHART DATA

Whether official or proprietary, the pricing of electronic chart data varies widely. In the USA, RNCs and ENCs are available for free, while for most HOs, official electronic chart data must be purchased. Some ECDIS manufacturers include a world-wide portfolio of proprietary electronic chart data along with the purchase of ECDIS equipment. Other manufacturers only provide a system (hardware and software) but recommend various sources of official or proprietary data that can be used. In addition, some companies offer a variety electronic chart data including ENCs, SENCs, RNCs, as well as proprietary formats. An overview of ENC services can be found in chapter 14.

a) ENC data

World-wide coverage and availability of official ENC data is nearly complete. A wide variety of services exist which are described in greater detail in chapter 14. ENC packaging and pricing vary greatly, and are constantly changing based on market forces. As such, current pricing/cost information should be obtained from the electronic chart data/service providers and chart agents.

For an estimate of cost of ENC data, a freight liner (e.g. container vessel) has been chosen operating on the route Europe-Australia/New Zealand as example. Use has been made of pre-defined folios for complete sea areas and of the flexibility offered by several ENC services to purchase data on demand from underway. This greatly reduces the number of ENCs to be purchased as basic stock. With these assumptions one can estimate the cost for an initial ENC fitting to about $10,000US per year. This may include the provision of all necessary updates, or in some cases, annual updating service is an additional cost.

b) Raster Navigational Charts (RNCs)

Use of raster data for navigation is allowed under the SOLAS regime only under certain operational restrictions, and only where ENCs do not exist yet. There are only few areas left where this is the case. As such, this RNCs would play only a local role and no longer need to be regarded as a significant cost for a SOLAS-compliant ECDIS.

22.3   Cost-benefit Analysis

Two cost-benefit studies showed significant benefits associated with the use of ECDIS. In 1994, the Canadian Coast Guard began installing 'Ship Electronic Chart and Navigation Systems' (SECANS) onboard 36 ships of its fleet. A cost-benefit analysis performed in 1998 indicated a positive net present value over a projected 10-year period [Leenhouts et al, 1998]. Direct benefits included fuel saving, engine movement reduction, and time savings. Indirect benefits were improved operational efficiency (e.g., search and rescue, ice breaking, servicing aids to navigation), decrease in delay days, and accidents avoided. Payback calculations indicated that the cost of procurement and installation would be recovered in approximately 21 months based on identified benefits from productivity gains. Overall, the study concluded that the cost-to-benefit ratio for installing ECDIS was 1:18

In 2003, the Norwegian Classification Society (DnV) performed a cost-benefit assessment to evaluate the effectiveness of implementing various risk control options (RCOs) intended to reduce the risk for large cruise vessels as a result of navigational errors.

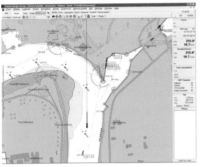
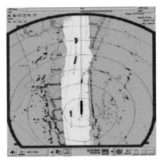

Figure 23.10: Inland ENC display of information and navigation mode
a) Inland ECDIS in information mode [Source: Tresco Engineering]
b) Inland ECDIS in information mode [Source: Innovative Navigation]

Inland ENCs
While there are some differences between the North American and European inland water-
ways, there are far more similarities. In this regard, in 2003 The Inland ENC Harmonization
Group (IEHG) was formed to facilitate the development of international standards for Inland
ENC data in North America and Europe. From 2005 to the present, IEHG has expanded to
include the Russian Federation, Brazil, Peoples Republic of China and the Republic of Korea.
The goal of the IEHG is to agree upon specifications for Inland ENCs that are suitable for all
known inland ENC data requirements for safe and efficient navigation, worldwide. The IEHG
works closely with the International Hydrographic Organization (IHO), and on 14 April 2009,
became recognized as a Non-Governmental International Organization (NGIO) of IHO. As an
NGIO, IEHG supports, advises and provides input to IHO regarding Inland ENC matters.

Similar to a "Maritime" ENC, an Inland ENC (IENC) is defined as:
the database, standardized as to content, structure and format, for use with inland electronic chart display
and/ or information systems operated onboard of vessels transiting inland waterways. An IENC is issued
by or on the authority of a competent government agency, and conforms to standards initially developed
by the International Hydrographic Organization (IHO) and refined by the Inland ENC Harmonization
Group. An IENC contains all the chart information necessary for safe navigation on inland waterways
and may contain supplementary information in addition to that contained in the paper chart (e.g. sailing
directions, machine-readable operating schedules, etc.) which may be considered necessary for safe navigation and voyage planning.

The framework for IENC standards [IEHG, 2008]
includes:
1. Use of IHO S-57 (Edition 3.1), including:
   'Maritime' ENC Product Specification (Appendix B1)
   Object Catalogue (Appendix A)
   Use of Object Catalogue (Appendix B.1, Annex A)
2. A minimum IENC Product Specification that includes mandatory requirements for safety-of-
   navigation on inland waterways, worldwide.
3. An IENC Encoding Guide that provides guidance on recommended object classes, attributes,
   and attribute values for encoding IENC data.

4. IENC Feature Catalogue.
5. Establishment of an IENC Register for additional real-world, IENC features, attributes, and enumerations that are not already contained in IHO S-57 Edition 3.1 Object Catalogue.
6. Use of the ienc.openecdis.org as a means of communication, and as an interim means to register additional IENC object classes, attributes, and attribute values.
7. Align with the future IHO S-100 Standard for Geospatial Data, when it becomes operational. In particular, this includes an IENC Register as part of the overall IHO Registry.

As of February 2010, the current versions of IENC-related standards [IEHG, 2008] are:
  IENC Product Specification, Ed. 2.2 (February 2010)
  Feature Catalogue, Ed. 2.2 (February 2010)
  IENC Encoding Guide, Ed. 2.2.0 (February 2010)
Two other Inland IENC-related standards that are not maintained by IEHG, but are used in Europe include:
  Inland ECDIS Standard, Ed. 2.2
  IENC Presentation Library, Ed. 2.2
Copies of all IENC-related standards available at: http://ienc.openecdis.org

23.5   Customised Types of ENCs

23.5.1   PORT ENC
Masters and pilots of vessels approaching a harbour/port normally use a combination of ship-borne ECDIS equipment and Portable Pilot Units (PPUs) to display geo-spatial navigation-related information. Official ENCs issued by national Hydrographic Offices are designed to meet the requirements of maritime navigation in open sea, coastal areas and approaches to harbour. However, in terms of information content, detail, compilation scale, accuracy, and land-based features, 'maritime' ENCs normally do not provide necessary information required for precise maneuvering, turning, berthing, or docking of increasingly large vessels in very confined waterways and port terminal facilities. One example is the official ENC of the Port of Hamburg (Germany). It meets all required IHO standards for maritime navigation. However, the chart data is too small in scale, contains little bathymetric information, and has limited horizontal accuracy for land-based topographic features (i.e. quay-walls, piers, and pontoons).

For a wide variety of port operations (e.g., dredging, vessel maneuvering/docking, under-keel clearance) there are data requirements for precise vertical and horizontal accuracy. This can be achieved by using modern surveying and remote sensing technologies. The data collected is used by the port authorities to produce detailed maps and planning documents. This same source data can be used by port authorities for charting purposes.

When a paper chart is used to produce 'maritime' ENCs, the compilation scale of the ENC cannot be greater than that of the source data (e.g., a paper nautical chart). Otherwise inaccuracies and errors would be introduced due to cartographic generalizations and digitizing errors. For a Port ENC, the source data are highly-accurate topographic and hydrographic surveys, and from precise digital aerial photos (orthophotos). As such, it is possible to have a compilation scale of 1:1000. When displayed on ECDIS or a PPU, the display scale can be 1:500 - 1:5,000.

– information about suppliers, logistic services and other services in a port and its vicinity
  which may be useful for the ship operator,
– road traffic information for the road networks of ports,
– public transportation networks in port cities,
– unfortunately, much of this information is disjointed, available in incompatible formats, dis-
  tributed on different media, or provided as disjointed service(s). The purpose of creating a
  Spatial Data Infrastructure (SDI) is to change this unsatisfactory situation by taking advantage
  of recent developments in information technology.

Spatial Data Infrastructure (SDI) has been defined as:

> "metadata[1], spatial data sets and spatial data services; network services and technologies; agreements on
> sharing, access and use; and coordination and monitoring mechanisms, processes and procedures, estab-
> lished, operated or made available" [EU INSPIRE, 2007].

The objective of SDI is clearly to facilitate the uses of geographic information regardless of
source and format, and to achieve the greatest possible interoperability. It therefore is made up
of the following basic components [Gruenreich, 2005]:
• geoportals acting as central entry points for public web access,
• geo-databases, consisting of metadata describing the data contents, reference data; defining
  the geodetic framework (see chapter 5), and thematic data,
• networks connecting, based on common standards, the geo-databases and related services
  through geo-portals,
• standards for unified or at least interoperable geodetic reference, data structure and data
  access.

SDI projects exist on many hierarchical levels from local national projects to regional or international level. An example is the Infrastructure for Spatial Information in the European Com-
munity (INSPIRE) Project where the 27 member states of the EU have agreed to work together
to establish a common SDI based on the same set of standards. The overarching goal is to form
the building blocks for a Global Spatial Data Infrastructure (GSDI). In this regard, an international association exists to further this global project. A number of examples of global geo-data
portals are already available (e.g., the United Nations Environmental Programme UNEP[2]).

To date, the primary focus for SDI has been driven by topographic mapping agencies. The first
steps towards marine infrastructure were specialised project networks that have been established under the umbrella of the UNESCO's Intergovernmental Oceanographic Commission
(IOC). This organization has maintained for many years a global network of 66 National
Oceanographic Data Centres. The purpose of these networks is scientific, to facilitate data
exchange between researchers, although some of the services offered by Data Centres are pub-
licly available.

---

1 'metadata' means information describing spatial data sets and spatial data services and making it possible
   to discover, inventory and use them
2 http://geodata.grid.unep.ch/]

In 2005, the International Hydrographic Organization took action on the rapidly growing relevance of SDI projects for hydrography. The keyword "Marine SDI" (MSDI) was coined describing the set of policies, standards and procedures appropriate for marine applications. This also included oceanography. Hydrographic offices have realised that their core business is collecting, administering, and processing spatial data of the marine environment. An obvious conclusion is that paper charts and ENCs, just as all other hydrographic products, are only products which can and should be derived from encompassing marine spatial data bases, rather than populating databases and ENCs from digitised charts and maps. By shifting the focus from derived products to marine databases, it becomes evident that supplying marine digital data will become in fact a potentially significant part of the overall business of digital data services As such, it has become important for HOs to align with national SDI initiatives thereby merging the range of land-based services with marine data services.

In 2009, the IHO developed policies to advise and assist its member states in the development of SDI [IHO C-17, 2009]. As an important contribution to any standards for MSDI, IHO completed the development of S-100 [IHO S-100, 2010] which IHO refers to as "The Universal Hydrographic Data Model". This ISO 191xx-compatible standard (see Chapter 4.3.5) lays the basis for the integration of the marine spatial data world into a truly global spatial data infrastructure.

Currently, the process of forming the global SDI covering both land and ocean is in its infancy. It is characterised by a multitude of projects and evolving thematic networks often controlled by global super projects such as the Global Earth Observation System of Systems (GEOSS). Numerous geo-portals and web-based services exist already today which can be used by service providers to offer specialised geo-data services to individual branches. Similar to those ENC Data Servers (see chapter 14) who compile ENCs from a variety of sources into single, integrated services, SDI establishes opportunities for service providers to develop wave forecasts, ocean current forecasts and observational data, e.g. ice coverage maps, from government sector into customised services, transmit these forecast data using e-Navigation communication onboard ship where commercial ECDIS add-ons process the data for route optimisation. Likewise, VTS Centres will be able to transmit real-time wind and current measurements at critical points along harbour approaches and within ports, available from an SDI-based real-time environmental data server, onboard ship for display on the ECDIS to assist the Navigator in decision making and maneuvering.

Building a service infrastructure as a task for the private sector will concentrate on issues of prime interest to ship owners. This includes increasing efficiency of ship operations, reducing voyage time and fuel consumption, saving harbour lay time, avoiding damages to cargo due to wash, etc. Such services will therefore concentrate on making voyage planning and voyage execution more efficient. To a large part, this will require additional customised and up-to-date geographic information, such as wind, current, sea state and ice routing data. The formation of MSDI – nationally, regionally and worldwide – is prerequisite for the development of a new maritime service market. These services are needed to provide the customised data services described above supporting voyage planning and voyage execution onboard ship, taking advantage of the fast expanding broadband communication facilities. This e-Navigation

Glossary

The following definitions are primarily taken from the IMO Performance Standards for ECDIS [IMO ECDIS PS, (1995) 2006], or the IHO Dictionary [S32AI] and the 'Glossary of ECDIS-related Terms' [IHO S32 (1994) 2010]. Some of the definitions have been simplified or shortened. Others have been modified to make them more understandable or to bring them up-to-date. Cross-references to other terms contained in this Glossary are shown in italics.

- **aid to navigation**
  Buoys, beacons, fog signals, lights, radio beacons, leading marks, radio position fixing systems, and generally any charted or otherwise published device serving the interests of safe navigation. An aid to navigation is a *navigational aid* which is external to a craft.

- **AIS: Automatic Identification System**
  A ship borne communication and identification system that provides automatically to appropriately equipped shore stations and other ships, information including the ship's identify, type, position, course, speed, navigational status, and other safety-related information. With AIS, a ship is able to automatically receive such information from similarly fitted ships and to exchange data with shore based facilities. Also, shore stations (e.g. VTS centers) can monitor and track ships movements.

- **alarm**
  In ECDIS a device or system which alerts by audible means, or audible and visual means, a condition requiring attention.

- **ARPA: Automatic Radar Plotting Aid**
  A system wherein radar targets are automatically acquired and tracked, and collision situations computer-assessed and warnings given.

- **attribute**
  A characteristic of an *object*, usually of a charted feature. It is implemented by a defined attribute label/code, acronym, definition and applicable values. In the data structure, the attribute is defined by its label/code. Attributes are either qualitative or quantitative. The attributes required for ECDIS are defined in Appendix A of the IHO Object Catalogue.

- **back-up arrangement**
  In ECDIS, facilities enabling safe take-over of ECDIS functions and measures facilitating means for safe navigation of the remaining part of the voyage in case of ECDIS failure.

- **cartographic object**
  A *feature object* which contains information about the cartographic representation (including text) of real world entities (*features*).

· **cell**
In ECDIS the basic unit of ENC data covering a defined geographical area bounded by two meridians and two parallels. The amount of chart information contained in a cell depends on its intended navigational purpose.

· **chain**
A sequence of one or more *edges*.

· **chain-node**
Data structure in which the geometry is described in terms of *edges*, isolated *nodes* and connected *nodes*. Edges and connected nodes are topologically linked. Nodes are explicitly coded in the data structure.

· **chart datum**
Short for chart sounding datum, it is a permanently established surface from which soundings or tide heights are referred. Sometimes called a vertical datum. It is a plane so low that the tide will not frequently fall below it. The 'Lowest Astronomical Tide' (LAT) has been adopted internationally as chart datum. However, other definitions (e.g. Mean Spring Low Water) are still in use. In areas where tides are not significant Mean Water Level is often used as chart datum.

· **collection object**
A *feature object* describing the relationship between other *objects*.

· **compilation scale**
The *scale* at which the ENC data was compiled. The compilation scale depends on the *navigational purpose* the ENC data is intended for and should be based on the respective standard radar ranges.

· **course**
The intended horizontal direction of travel. It is measured from 0° at the reference direction clockwise through 360°; strictly for marine navigation, the term applies to the direction to be steered, which sometimes differs from the direction intended to be made good over the ground. The course is designated as true, magnetic, compass, or grid as the reference direction is true, magnetic, compass or grid north respectively.

· **course made good (CMG)**
the actual *track* made good over the ground (seabed); the direction of the point of arrival from the point of departure. Course made good is the direction component of the resultant ship's velocity and the water current. Course made good should not be confused with *heading*, or ship's head.

· **course over ground (COG)**
The direction of the path over the ground actually followed by a vessel. It is normally a somewhat irregular line. This is a misnomer in that courses are directions steered or intended to be steered through the water with respect to a reference meridian. Also called *track over ground*.

· **course up display**
In ECDIS (or radar) the information shown on the *display* with the direction of the vessel's course upward. The display orientation is stabilised by means of the gyro until a new *course* direction is fed in. Course-up orientation avoids the disadvantages with the *head-up display* due to yawing or other changes in heading.

· **cursor-pick**
The process of querying a point-symbol, line or area for further information from the data base which is not represented by the symbol.